Reading Manga:
How to Follow

Each page of a graphic novel is divided into boxes called panels. You follow the panels from left to right and top to bottom, like this:

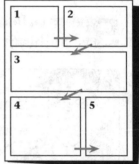

Each panel is like a paragraph in a regular book. It shows you where the characters are, and what they are doing, saying and thinking.

Some panels include a little box at the top (or the bottom), giving you information about what's going on. These are called captions.

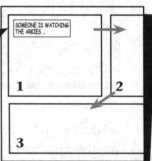

SOMEONE IS WATCHING THE ARKIES ...

DID YOU KNOW?

Traditional Japanese manga look a little different. That's because in Japan, people read from right to left. Japanese manga is read like this:

It's easier than it looks!

Reading Manga: Who's talking?

Speech balloons tell you who is speaking, what they're saying, and how.

Sometimes the lettering changes, to tell you which words are most important. These words might appear in **BOLD** or LARGE TYPE or in *ITALICS*.

Sometimes a punctuation point is enough to explain what's going on.

And how would you show an alien language? Maybe like this:

Reading Manga:
What's that sound?

When you read speech bubbles, you hear manga characters' voices inside your head. There's a way to hear the background noises too – the rumble of thunder, the ringing of a telephone, the crack of a stick underfoot.

Manga artists represent sound effects (or SFX) by placing words over the panels, using lettering to suit each particular sound. It looks like this:

Scary sound

Mechanical sound

Quiet sound

DID YOU KNOW?

Japanese manga SFX are very precise. For example, *bicha bicha* means small splash, *bashan* is a medium splash, and *zaban* is a very big splash. There's even an SFX phrase for total silence: *shiin*.

SFX are used to show emotions as well. The word *unzori* placed next to a character tells you they're feeling bored. If it was *moji moji* they'd be feeling shy, and *shobo shobo* indicates sadness.

Reading Manga:

What's that look on your face?

Manga characters have exaggerated expressions, to help you understand what they're feeling. The first feature everyone notices is the eyes, which may be wide open in:

Shock

Fear

Hope

Closed eyes can mean:

Laughter

Sadness

Noses and chins are more difficult to spot (some characters have no nose at all). This reflects the Japanese preference for delicate features. In manga, big noses and chins are kept for the bad guys.

Reading Manga:
What's that look on your face?

Just like manga characters' eyes, manga mouths are either huge or tiny. A big, wide-open mouth indicates:

Fear   Anger   Happiness

A character with a little mouth may be feeling:

Sad   Thoughtful   Shy

You can also tell a lot about manga characters from the crazy colour or style of their hair. For example, blue hair can mean the character is cool-headed, while orange hair equals determination (and sometimes a fiery temper). Wild, spiky hairstyles show the character is adventurous.

Characters

Spartans

Perry

Perry tries to be sensible – he really does.
But he can't say no to an adventure.

Fasool

Fasool is a hot-head. He often leads Perry into trouble –
if Perry doesn't lead him there first.

Sergeant Zach

Perry's uncle, he is one of the troopers who
patrol *Spartan*. He tries (but fails) to keep
the boys out of strife.

Other Folk

Sheaths and Daggers
The Darken twins,
junior mobsters.

Space Pirates
Intergalactic thieves. A bad lot.

THE KIDS SEE THAT SPARTAN IS HURTLING TOWARDS THE SUN.

FORBIDDEN ZONE

THE ESCAPE PODS WILL NEVER CLEAR THE SUN'S GRAVITY.

SO MUCH FOR THAT IDEA!

I NEED VOLUNTEERS. THE MOST CAPABLE CADETS HAVE TO HELP US SAVE SPARTAN.

SHEATHS AND DAGGERS, COME WITH US. THE REST OF YOU LOOK FOR ANY SIGN OF LIFE.

HUH. I DON'T REMEMBER VOLUNTEERING.

TWO KIDS DASH AROUND THE CORNER.

WE'VE FOUND ALL THE ADULTS. THEY'RE IN THE BUBBLE.

AND THEY'VE BEEN HIT WITH IMMOBILISER DARTS!

THE BUBBLE IS A HUGE STADIUM, USED FOR GAMES LIKE ROCKETBOARD.

THIS CHANGES THINGS. WHAT OR WHO DID THIS? IT DIDN'T JUST HAPPEN.

NICE ONE, SMART GUY. NOW WHAT?

YEAH. YOU WANNA BE THE BOSS? START THINKING!

RIGHT. WE NEED TO GET TO THE BRIDGE. MEANWHILE, EVERYONE SPREAD OUT. REPORT ANY PIRATES!

PERRY, FASOOL AND THE TWINS HEAD FOR THE BRIDGE. THEY PASS AN EXTERNAL VIEWSCREEN...

FASOOL, DO YOU SEE WHAT I SEE?

YEAH.

YES. THE BOYS SEE A FLAT, LEAN, MEAN-LOOKING SHIP, CLINGING LIKE A LIMPET TO THE BULGE OF THE COMMAND BRIDGE.

PIRATES! I HATE IT WHEN I'M RIGHT.

ME TOO.

JUST AS WELL YOU'RE WRONG MOST OF THE TIME, LOSER. GRRRR.

- 14 -

ATTENTION ALL HANDS. ATTENTION ALL HANDS. MONSTERS ARE ON THE LOOSE. I REPEAT, MONSTERS ARE ON THE LOOSE! APPROACH WITH EXTREME CARE.

SOMETHING'S NOT RIGHT. WE NEED TO GET ON BOARD THAT PIRATE SHIP.

AS THEY CREEP DOWN THE COMPANIONWAY, THE KIDS OVERHEAR SOMETHING.

I WISH THE OTHERS WOULD HURRY UP. IF WE GET MUCH CLOSER TO THAT SUN, WE'RE ALL FRIED.

YEAH, I CAN'T WAIT TO DITCH THIS RUST BUCKET!

BLAH BLAH BLAH.

HAW! HAW! HAW!

THE GUARDS BLABBER EVERYTHING THE SPARTANS NEED TO KNOW. THE PIRATES PLAN TO STEAL EVERYTHING VALUABLE FROM SPARTAN THEN LEAVE IT TO ATOMISE IN THE SUN!

chapter 2 : The Old Shape-Shifting Moleculiser Trick

GGRRRRRRRRRR

PERRY AND FASOOL HURRY TO THE PIRATE SHIP...

...AND FIND IT EMPTY.

WHERE IS EVERYONE?

WHY WOULD THEY LEAVE NO-ONE ABOARD? UNLESS...

EXACTLY, FASOOL! THERE AREN'T MANY OF THEM AND THEY'RE USING...

...A SHAPE-SHIFTING MOLECULISER TO MAKE THEM LOOK BIGGER!

- 21 -

SHEATHS AND DAGGERS? IT'S ALL RIGHT? THAT DOESN'T ADD UP.

STAY BEHIND US, EVERYONE. THE FATE OF SPARTAN IS IN OUR HANDS!

COOL!

IT'S TIME TO WIN SPARTAN BACK! THE GROUP GROWS BIGGER...

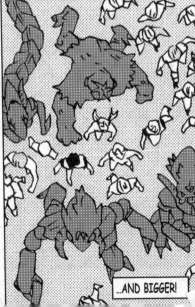

...AND BIGGER!

- 30 -

Space Pirates Spartapedia

Cadets Junior members of *Spartan*'s military – like Perry and Fasool.

Escape pods Emergency escape vehicles.

Immobiliser darts Darts with tranquillisers in their tips.

Restricted sector Area of *Spartan* that is off-limits to most Spartans.

Space Pirates Men and women who raid ships in space.

Spartan A huge space-faring ship.

Shape-shifting moleculiser A machine that allows people to change their shape.

Viewscreen An audio-visual monitor that shows what's happening in other parts of *Spartan*.

Zambisies An alien race.